WHAT MATTERS
in the end

WHAT MATTERS
in the end

End of Life Care

Louise Morse, MA (CBT)

Contributors:
Emma Hughes, RN
Dr Judy McClaren
Dr Sarah Jones

PILGRIMS'
FRIEND
SOCIETY

What Matters in the End

End of Life Care

Copyright April 2016 the Pilgrims' Friend Society.

A catalogue record for this publication is available from the British Library

ISBN: 978-0-9930148-9-5

Designed and typeset by: Pete Barnsley (Creativehoot.com)

Printed and bound by Nørhaven, Denmark

First published in the UK in 2016 by
the Pilgrims' Friend Society

175 Tower Bridge Road, London SE1 2AL.
Tel +44 0300 303 1400

Email: info@pilgrimsfriend.org.uk
Website: www.pilgrimsfriend.org.uk

Distributed by the Pilgrims' Friend Society

PREFACE

THE AIM of this booklet is to encourage readers of all ages to have conversations about end of life care and dying with people who matter to them long before circumstances make it necessary.

When the time comes lots of things seem to happen at once, but the one thing you can do as a family is to decide on what is important to you, and be prepared well in advance. Then not only do you have a road-map that will help you navigate through unfamiliar and difficult terrain, but you will be able to avoid the regrets that can come when things are left too late. And thinking about the inevitability of death may prompt us to live life to the full, while we can.

People are often hesitant about bringing up the topic of end of life care with their parents or elderly relatives for fear they may upset them with thoughts of death, or even be seen to be anticipating the worst for them. But it can be an opportunity to reassure, to remind ourselves again of what Jesus did at Calvary for fallen humanity and for the reality of life with Him in Heaven. When He answered the thief who was dying on the cross next to His, Jesus said to him that 'today you will be with me in Paradise.' Luke 23:43

Jesus the Way, the Truth and the Life

'Let not your hearts be troubled. Believe in God; believe also in me. In my Father's house are many rooms. If it were not so, would I have told you that I go to prepare a place for you? And if I go and prepare a place for you, I will come again and will take you to myself, that where I am you may be also. And you know the way to where I am going.'

John 14: 1-5 (ESV)

'But just as it is written, "Things which eye has not seen and ear has not heard, And which have not entered the heart of man, all that God has prepared for those who love Him.'

1 Corinthians 2:9 (ESV)

'Oh, how abundant is your goodness, which you have stored up for those who fear you and worked for those who take refuge in you, in the sight of the children of mankind!'

Psalm 31:19 (ESV)

CONTENTS

INTRODUCTION

This booklet looks at the practical, spiritual and psychological issues surrounding end of life care. It draws together observations and recommendations made by a former old age medical consultant, a General Practitioner, a nurse with a special interest and experience in end of life care, and a Christian cognitive behavioural therapist, as well as findings from recent studies.

It is written primarily within a Christian context. The believer's view of death is different to that of non-believers: the one looks on it as a step to eternal life and joys unimaginable, and the other sees it as a full stop to life of any kind. In between there are those who have different beliefs as to what lies beyond death, but for every person on earth there is acknowledgement of one inescapable fact: everyone will experience the dying process. We will all know the dissolution of the 'earthly tent' (2 Corinthians 5:1). Apart from being born and being 'born again' as Christians (John 3: 1-21) it is arguably the most significant event in life, yet is the least discussed or considered until we feel it drawing near. It's a topic that is coming under the spotlight as older people approach the end of their lives. We may not like to think about it in our sixties, or seventies, but it creeps into our consciousness as we become frailer in our late eighties or nineties.

Older old keen to talk

In contrast, a study of a group of people aged over 95 by the Department of Public Health and Primary Care at the University of Cambridge found that they were keen to discuss dying and end of life care, but were seldom asked their opinion (PLOS ONE, 6.4.16).

Some participants felt they were a nuisance to others, and some wanted desperately to reach the end, suggesting they had simply lived too long. One woman described herself as the 'lady-in-waiting, waiting to go.'

Lead author, Dr Jane Fleming, said that despite the increase in the number of people living into very old age, there is far too little discussion about what the 'oldest old' feel about the end of their lives. It's a sad reflection on those who care for them that they are not listened to, and not consulted about something so important.

In the last few years the NHS and charities like the Marie Curie and Macmillan Trust have been publicising end of life care, and in 2015 the NHS attempted to find out from the elderly and the disabled where they would choose to die. There has been much attention drawn to the poor end of life care many have received in our hospitals, and steps are being taken, such as training nursing staff, to rectify this.

In June 2014 the Leadership Alliance for the Care of Dying People issued a document for NHS guidance and policy. Among its Prompts for Practice is an instruction named, 'Plan and Do,' which includes food and drink, symptom control and psychological, social and *'spiritual suppor*t … co-ordinated and delivered with compassion.' We look further at the document in the 'What to Expect' section.

To be swallowed up by life

In Pilgrims' Friend Society's care homes there is little reticence amongst residents when it comes to talking about dying. Despite the loving care they receive, many echo the apostle Paul's sentiment that 'while we are in this tent, we groan and are burdened, because we do not wish to be unclothed but to be clothed instead with our heavenly dwelling, so that what is mortal may be swallowed up by life,' (2 Corinthians 5:4). In our Tunbridge Wells home a lady who lived to the age of 107 used to ask the manager, 'Why am I still here? Why hasn't the Lord taken me?'. It's not uncommon for an older Christian to share Paul's longings.

Dying is not often a 'tidy' experience, as GP Judy McClaren points out. Death is the result of sin and is not always as we would want it to be. We can, however, make our wishes known, and this is discussed in Advance Planning.

Bethany care home manager Emma Hughes qualified as a nurse in the 1980s. A major change she has seen in those years is that people are now encouraged to make decisions about their last days, and to make their wishes known. She said, 'We are now very much advised to give people the opportunity to tell us what they want, indeed to encourage them to do so. We call this Advance Care Planning. I am so pleased to discover that this really works, and people and their relatives find it reassuring.'

Residents at the Bethany home have welcomed

the opportunity to talk about their wishes in this context. These included where they wanted to die, whether they wanted someone with them and who they wished those to be; favourite Bible passages that they wanted to have read to them, whether they wanted music to listen to and their choice, even what they wanted the people who were sitting with them to do – to sit quietly, talk to them, or read to them.

Death is God's Providence

Professor John Wyatt, retired Professor of Ethics and Perinatology at University College London and author of books on ethical issues, writes that 'in the biblical narrative human lifespan is limited, not just as a curse, but out of God's grace.

'To live for ever in a fallen and decaying body is not a blessing, but a curse. So in God's providence, death may be a merciful release from an existence trapped in a disintegrating body. Not only that, the Christian faith helps us to see that dying need not be a totally negative experience…. The end of our lives on this earth may be transformed by God's grace into an opportunity for growth and internal healing. We need to emphasise that dying is really a spiritual event, even if it has medical implications.' (*Evangelicals*

Now, September 2015.) He observes that in the New Testament it is very significant that believers are not described as 'dying', instead they 'fall asleep'.

Perhaps thinking more about our dying might prompt us to live more purposefully until then. Residents spend an average of 18 months in PFS care homes, and our aim is to enable them to live as fully as they can. Our experience shows that fruitful living is possible right to the very end of life. We can realise how finite our lives are, and how important it is to make each day count (Psalm 90:12). Christian Country singer Tim McGraw wrote a song about a father who, after being given a terminal diagnosis, lived more intensely than ever before. He 'loved deeper, and spoke sweeter, and gave forgiveness he'd been denying', adding that 'someday I hope you get the chance to live like you were dying.' It's worth listening to: http://www.metrolyrics.com/live-like-you-were-dying-lyrics-tim-mcgraw.html

WHY THE RIGHT TIME TO TALK ABOUT DYING IS NOW

For a long time, talking about death and dying has been taboo in our culture. We don't want to upset our dear ones by raising a topic that is seen to be morbid. Yet among Christians this is not how it should be. It was a point raised vigorously by a Christian GP at a national conference. 'Why are Christians afraid of dying?' she asked. It may be, as American surgeon Atul Gawande observes in his seminal book, *Being Mortal, Medicine and what Matters in the End,* because people only die once, and have no experience to draw on. We are fearful of the unknown.

But in the Bible, believers have a body of wisdom to draw on. We also have the power of the Holy Spirit within us, 'who is the guarantee of our inheritance until we acquire possession of it, to the praise of his glory,' Ephesians 1:14. He is a pledge, a down payment, a foretaste of the good things to come.

'Oh death where is your victory? Oh death where is your sting?' proclaims Paul in his letter to the Christians at Corinth (1 Corinthians 15:55). In another letter he wrote, 'So we are always of good courage. We know that while we are at home in the body we are away from the Lord, for we walk by faith, not by sight. Yes, we are of good courage, and we would rather be away from the body and at home with the Lord,' (2 Corinthians 5:6-8). The New Testament saints we read about are now all at home with the Lord, including Paul. And many of us 'walking by faith' have dear ones who are also at home with Him.

Atul Gawande found that patients who had 'substantive discussions with their doctors about their end of life preferences were far more likely to die at peace, and in control of their situation.' Significantly, he found that it was *the discussion*, not the list of issues that mattered most. At the end of their lives he found that people wanted to 'share their memories, pass on wisdom and keepsakes, settle relationships, establish their legacies, make peace with God and ensure that those who are left behind will be okay.'

It is better to discuss something as emotive as our dying *before* emotions are stirred by receiving a terminal diagnosis or when it is clear that you are coming to the end of your life. Genesis 24 and Hebrews 11:20-22 describe how Joseph gave instructions concerning his burial. In the same way Jacob, his father, had made his end of life wishes clearly known.

We need to talk about dying when we are healthy and young, says Palliative Care Nurse Jill Hardman-Smith*. In the following chapter are some thoughts and choices to help you think about what is important to you.

---

* (www.eastmidlands.nhs.uk/timetotalk)

How lovely is your dwelling place,
  O Lord of hosts!
My soul longs, yes, faints
  for the courts of the Lord;
my heart and flesh sing for joy
  to the living God.
Even the sparrow finds a home,
  and the swallow a nest for herself,
  where she may lay her young,
at your altars, O Lord of hosts,
  my King and my God.
Blessed are those who dwell in your house,
  ever singing your praise!
Blessed are those whose strength is in you,
  in whose heart are the highways to Zion
As they go through the Valley of Baca
  they make it a place of springs;
  the early rain also covers it with pools.
They go from strength to strength;
  each one appears before God in Zion.

—Psalm 84: 1-7

WHAT MATTERS THE MOST

These are the priorities about their end of life care that people we know in our care homes and others have said are important to them. They also include findings of a study by Age Concern, 1999. They are points for considering and discussing with the people in your life.

People want to -

- be without suffering

- be in control, conscious and thinking clearly

- be in the place of their choice

- not be a burden

- have a sense of completion

- have dignity and privacy

- have time to say goodbye, and control over aspects of timing

- have access to whatever expertise and information is required

- have access to hospice care in any location

- have emotional and spiritual support

- be able to strengthen relationships with close family and friends

- know that their loved ones are going to be alright

- know when death is coming, and to understand what is to be expected

- have no unresolved issues, including emotional, psychological or spiritual

- have empathetic and skilled carers

- be able to make their own choices at the time, including whom they wish to be with them, and when

- be able to leave when it's time to go and not have life prolonged needlessly

- know that their wishes for their funerals, or any other after-death arrangements, including their Wills are in place, and will be honoured.

Time and place and not being a burden

There can be a balance between the effects of pain control medication and the person retaining consciousness, in order to exercise a measure of control, according to Emma Hughes. 'I am saddened by how many people tell us that they are frightened of dying in pain,' she said, 'with good pain control this should not happen.'

Dr Sarah Jones notes that the link between feelings and physical health is not always appreciated. It can be relatively straightforward to deal with physical pain and other symptoms, but there can be other issues such as emotional pain and difficulties with family relationships.

The timing of death is not predictable, and it often influences the place where we die. Knowing when someone is in the last few weeks or days of life can be particularly difficult to predict.

As mentioned earlier, in 2015 the NHS attempted to gather information from people who were seen to be vulnerable, including the elderly and the disabled, as to where they would like to die. At the time it was portrayed as a blunt, insensitive exercise, but the aim was to allocate resources so that people's wishes would be respected, as far as possible. In 2015 statistics showed that 54 percent of all deaths occurred in hospitals; 40 percent of which, it is believed, could have happened elsewhere, and that up to 70 percent of people do not die where they would have chosen to.

It is sad that Christians say they do not wish to be a burden, when the Scriptures tell us to bear one another's burdens. Indeed, we are told that doing this 'fulfils the law of Christ,' Galatians 6:2. How can we bear one another's burdens if we are not prepared to be a burden? It is something to discuss with close relatives, sensitively and openly.

It is good to have no unresolved issues at any time of our lives, but it can be especially important at the very end. To know that forgiveness is not being withheld, for example, and to be able to tell loved ones how much they mean to you, can release a deep sense of peace, as does knowing that they are going to be alright.

Reassurance that it's time to let go

Sometimes, families need to give the dying person 'permission to let go,' says Emma. 'When we are close to a dying person, we need to remember that even when all other ways of communicating have gone, it can well be the case that they can still hear us. We need to be careful what we say, not talk over the person and involve them in what we are saying.' She gives an example of a mother who was comfortable, but looked a little worried. She could no longer speak, but there were signs that she could still hear. Her adult children were sitting around her bed, and told her what a great Mum she had been and that they would look after each other. Emma recalls, 'She smiled a gentle smile, nodded her head slightly and sighed. She needed to hear those words before she could let go, which wasn't long afterward.'

Throughout our lives we are aware that our 'earthly tent' is decaying. We see it and feel it. But at the same time we know that the essence of ourselves, our eternal being within is being transformed from one degree of glory to another (2 Corinthians 3:18). The Holy Spirit within us is making us more like Him – and after the dying of the body we will see Him, and will be like Him.

And I heard a voice from heaven saying, "Write this down: Blessed are those who die in the Lord from now on. Yes, says the Spirit, they are blessed indeed, for they will rest from their hard work; for their good deeds follow them!"

—**Revelation 14:13**

ADVANCE STATEMENT

There are said to be five important issues to consider as life draws towards its end -

- Legal and financial matters,

- Organ donation,

- End of life care,

- How you would like to be remembered,

- Funeral plans

This booklet deals with end of life care.

When a resident comes into one of our care homes staff draw up what is known as a Care Plan. It's drawn up together with the person and their relatives, and is quite wide ranging and comprehensive.

An Advance Statement is a document in which you record your specific wishes for your end of life care. It doesn't mean that hospitals or care homes are legally bound to abide by it – and in fact may be prevented by circumstances on occasion, but they will do their best to respect your wishes.

An Advance Decision is a decision to refuse specific treatment, and is sometimes known as a Living Will. You may choose not to be resuscitated or to receive life-prolonging treatment. Sometimes, it can be clear to the medical team that treatment is not helping a patient's condition and that they are beginning to die and in these circumstances the doctors may decide to begin to withdraw these treatments.

The Welsh Assembly Government has decided that unless a person deliberately opts out of the scheme, when they die their organs can be harvested for transplanting to another person. This is not the case in England or Scotland, but it is something for you to consider – and to make your wishes known in advance.

You can say clearly where you wish to die.

You can state your preferences on all issues that are important to you. For example, who would you like to be with you – or would you prefer to be alone?

You can list the people you would like to be contacted if you were too ill to do it yourself.

Write down what sort of spiritual support would

be meaningful to you. Would it be Scripture reading, or music, or designated people to come and pray?

Would you like your family to plan to have a kind of 'shift system' to be with you? It would prevent you being overwhelmed and also give them time to rest, and to pray. Families need to take care of themselves and each other as this can be an exhausting time for them, emotionally and physically.

It's good to prepare this Advanced Statement with your loved ones, but remember, this is about what is important to you, in circumstances that you haven't experienced before. It's good to discuss it with others, and to take time to pray about it.

*But I do not account my life of
any value nor as precious to*

*myself, if only I may finish my
course and the ministry that*

*I received from the Lord Jesus,
to testify to the gospel of*

the grace of God.'

—Acts 20:24 (ESV)

WHAT TO EXPECT

In a care home

Good hospice care is normal in our residential care homes. Our Plymouth home manager, Emma Hughes, trained with St. Luke's, the local hospice, in what is known as The Six Steps to Success Course.

The Six Steps are –

1. Discussions as end of life approaches

2. Assessment, care planning and review

3. Co-ordination of care

4. Delivery of high quality care

5. Care in the last days of life

6. Care after death

The steps look quite dry and clinical but have deep implications. It means they call for training for staff and expert management.

When elderly people come into care they are

usually quite frail, and anticipate that it will be their last home before they enter Heaven. A former missionary and leprosy surgeon who lived in housing in the Evington Home before moving into care described it as the 'saints' marshalling yard before the ascent to Glory'. Residents usually prefer to die in their familiar room in their care home, without having vigorous medical interventions to prolong life. An example was 93 year old Percy, in our Brighton home. His GP had advised him that he could have surgery on a faulty valve in his heart, but Percy turned it down, saying he wanted to be comfortable and go Home to be with the Lord. When a resident dies in one of our homes our staff also support relatives and friends.

In your own home

It makes sense for people to be cared for by people who know them, and understand what is important to them. Most people would prefer to die at home, supported by a good care team and family members who understand their illness and know what to do.

The key to a good, peaceful death in your own home depends on the coordination of a number of different agencies, including the person's GP, the District Nurses, perhaps Macmillan Nurses and Marie Curie and others, and there needs to be a good coordinator. GP Dr Judy McLaren says that the aim is to have seamless care, 'which is not so easy now that GPs do not cover their own patients at the weekend. For example, there was an instance where a refusal to give 'top up' medication caused and led to increased patient distress and caused admission to hospital. The GP overruled, but by then arrangements had been made'. A 'hospice pack' containing syringe drivers and 'just in case' medications are very helpful to avoid panic and lack of medication at the weekends and at night.

Support for Carers

The Social Care Institute for Excellence (SCIE) urges all agencies to 'Think family' and consider how support for carers can impact on care for the patient. Carers are usually close family members, and don't think of themselves as carers. They should be seen as central partners in care who need to know about their loved one's medical condition and how it is likely to develop; be trained to carry out basic nursing tasks, and know how they can obtain help at any time. They should also have a 'key worker'; a named professional who can help them in accessing health and social care services, equipment and support. And equally important will be bereavement support after the death of the care recipient. Much informaton is given on the SCIE website: www.scie.org.uk, the link is: http://bit.ly/1ZN8sQP.

There needs to be sensitivity when talking to family members. 'Denial is a coping mechanism,' Dr McLaren advises, 'and should be respected.'

Good palliative care is recognised as vital in the end of life care package. Organisations that can advise and help are Marie Curie, who offer care and support through terminal illness (www.mariecurie.org.uk): the website link is: http://bit.ly/1rD1HWv.

Also the Macmillan Trust, (www.macmillan.org.uk): http://bit.ly/1VE8QSI.

The Admiral Nurses help with people with dementia and have a Helpline (found at the www.dementiauk.org website: website link http://bit.ly/21hSP4D.

And there is also good information at the Carers Trust UK (http://www.carersuk.org): website link: http://bit.ly/1SNBIV9.

In Hospital

Although most people would prefer to die in their own home, as mentioned earlier, death is not always orderly or tidy. Sometimes medical intervention is essential, which can mean going into hospital. In June 2014 the Leadership Alliance for the Care of Dying people issued guidance for Health and Care Staff, with prompts for practice.

It lists five Prompts for Practice, which include recognising the fact that death may be imminent and should be 'communicated clearly', including conversations between staff and the dying person and those important to them. Other factors are similar to those for dying in a care home – involving the person and relatives in decisions about treatment to the extent that the dying person wishes, meeting their needs, and having an individual plan of care which includes food and drink, symptom control and psychological, social and spiritual support. All this should be delivered with compassion. A pdf with full guidelines is available at http://www.nhsiq. nhs.uk/media/2485900/duties and responsibilities of health and care staff - with prompts for practice.pdf.

All NHS hospitals have chaplains who can be called on for spiritual help and support.

If relatives are unhappy with the care their loved one is receiving in hospital, they can talk to the hospital's Patient Advice and Liaison Service (PALS). Or the local NHS Complaints Advocacy Services – your local Council will have their address and telephone numbers.

CHRISTIANS COMING ALONGSIDE

Many local churches have trained visitors and listeners who will offer time and care to the dying and bereaved. And it is a Christian responsibility to support families who are caring for a loved one at the end of life. If the person is known in his or her fellowship then supporting them and their family can be a natural extension of Christian friendship and ministry.

Grief is a natural part of bereavement. The Scriptures tell us to identify with how others are feeling, and to have compassion. 'Weep with those who weep,' says Romans 12:15. Adjusting to life without their loved one begins even before the actual death. Sometimes just 'being there' for the person, saying very little but being prepared to listen, actively, can be all that is needed. Yet though we grieve, it is not as those who have no hope of the resurrection of the dead (1 Thessalonians 4:13).

The Christian whose life has been rooted and grounded in Christ will be encouraged by the Scriptures that talk about eternal life. 'So I say that we have confidence. And we really want to be away from this body and be at home with the Lord,' Paul wrote to the believers at Corinth (2 Corinthians 5:8).

Coming alongside families and the person who is dying can be very effective in a series of small touches. Little things like an appropriate card saying that you are thinking about them, or a telephone call, or even taking around a baked cake or a meal can say a great deal. The important thing is to ask what they would like. It could be help with the shopping or collecting the laundry or a prescription. Even if they say there is nothing they need, you have let them know that they are not forgotten; and that you are there for them. And most of all, pray that they may know the peace of God that passes all understanding. (Philippians 4:7).

For I am persuaded, that neither death, nor life, nor angels, nor principalities, nor powers, nor things present, nor things to come, nor height, nor depth, nor any other creature, shall be able to separate us from the love of God, which is in Christ Jesus our Lord.

— Romans 8:38-39 KJV

'There are duties which we owe to all men, arising out of a common nature; but the tie of a more sacred relationship established by God Himself binds us to believers'.

John Calvin, 1509-1564

'Old people are apt to be regarded as burdens, whereas it should be a joy and a privilege to minister to them. For this reason I specially commend the Charity to young people'.

**The Earl of Shaftesbury, KG,
at the Charity's Annual General Meeting, 1883.**

ABOUT THE PILGRIMS' FRIEND SOCIETY

PFS is a Christian charity with roots going back to August 1807, when the Aged Pilgrims' Friend Society (APFS) was formed by a group of young believers in Islington, London. 1807 was also the year that the Slave Trade Act received its royal assent abolishing the slave trade in the British colonies and making it illegal to carry enslaved people in British ships. Convinced of the value of every individual to God, anti-slave campaigner William Wilberforce, a generous supporter of the charity, became vice president from 1824 until his death in 1835. Other notable Christian friends and benefactors included the Earl of Shaftesbury and the preacher Charles Haddon Spurgeon, who preached sermons on APFS' behalf.

In the early 1800s there was no Welfare State and living conditions in Great Britain were dire. It was the time of the industrial revolution, which brought many people into the cities to earn a living. Children were working in factories and still sweeping chimneys. Elderly people were particularly vulnerable. The founders of APFS report many living in garrets and sleeping on straw, usually possessing only one garment. In those days APFS helped by giving regular pensions, which were always delivered in person, together with spiritual support. The first financial period closed on March 31st, 1808, with a total expenditure of £5 2s. 9d, and by the close of 1830, APFS had paid out in pensions £7,643.16.0d.

The first housing scheme was built in 1835. Today, PFS has sixteen housing and care schemes in different parts of the country, with around 500 people under its wing. A good percentage have dementia, and staff receive specialist training in dementia care. Each scheme also benefits from groups of supporters, known as 'Friends of ...' who visit and befriend residents and pray for staff. They also receive training in visiting those with dementia. Spiritual support remains a core component of care, and is particularly important for people with dementia and their families.

In addition, PFS helps to support the care of older people in the community by sharing its knowledge and experience with others at conferences and workshops around the country.

More information about this is given on page 39.

'Nevertheless, I am continually with you;
you hold my right hand.

You guide me with your counsel,
and afterward you will receive me to glory.

Whom have I in heaven but you?
And there is nothing on earth that I desire
besides you.

My flesh and my heart may fail,
but God is the strength of my heart and my
portion forever.'

Psalm 73: 22-26

RECOMMENDED READING

Dying with Grace
Judson Cornwall
Charisma Media, ISBN 1591854539

The Art of Dying, Living fully into the life to come
Rob Moll
IVP Books, ISBN-10: 0-8308-3736-1

Death and the Life After
Billy Graham
Thomas Nelson, ISBN-10: 0849911230

The Heaven Answer Book
Billy Graham
Thomas Nelson, ISBN-13: 978-1400319381

Where I Am: Heaven, Eternity, and Our Life Beyond
Billy Graham
Thomas Nelson, ISBN-10: 0718042220

Nearing Home: Life, Faith, and Finishing Well
Billy Graham
Thomas Nelson, ISBN-10: 0849948320

On Death and Dying:
What the dying have to teach doctors, nurses, clergy and their own families
Elisabeth Kübler-Ross
ISBN-10: 1476775540

Dr Kubler-Ross' greatest professional legacy was teaching the practice of humane care for the dying and the importance of unconditional love. She was the co-founder of the Hospice Movement.

Heaven

Randy Acorn

Tyndale House Publishers,
ISBN-10: 0842379428

Coping with bereavement

royalvoluntaryservice.org.uk

www.royalvoluntaryservice.org.uk/

HelpGuide.org

http://www.helpguide.org/articles/grief-loss/coping-with-grief-and-loss.htm

Coping with bereavement

http://www.nhs.uk/Livewell/
bereavement/Pages/coping-with-
bereavement.aspx

This is what participants have said about PFS conferences and seminars:

- *'At a subsequent meeting of the team, words such as 'uplifting' and 'encouraging' were used,and we all felt we had a much clearer understanding of dementia and how we could more effectively minister to sufferers and their families.'*

- *'Really helpful practical advice that I can apply.'*

- *'Really good at addressing practical issues that we raised.'*

- *'In my 25 years as a nurse, this was the best training day I have experienced.'*

- *'This has far exceeded our expectations in terms of content, delivery, and relevance to our real lives.'*

- *'Biblically and researched based: one of the best seminars I have ever heard.'*

- *'Lots of ideas of how to add value to the seniors work in our church.'*

- *'Very informative, full of hope and love and with the power of the Holy Spirit shining through.'*

- *'A good, interactive workshop: useful to understand the positive aspects of ageing as well as the issues with dementia.'*

TALKS AND SEMINARS AVAILABLE FROM THE PILGRIMS' FRIEND SOCIETY:

1. Making a truly dementia friendly church
2. Dementia – practical and spiritual insights
3. Dementia – the support and help that churches can give
4. Early dementia and the vital circles of support
5. Visiting people with dementia
6. Giving effective support to family caregivers
7. Empowering and engaging older people
8. How churches can effectively support dementia families
9. Caregivers – how to care for yourselves
10. Ministering in care homes
11. Dealing with loneliness
12. How to prepare for a great old age

13. Knowing when to downsize and how to do it

14. Developing your talents and gifting
    after retirement

15. Empowering older people

16. Caring for parents and other older relatives

17. Building communities, a street at a time

18. Christians and retirement

19. End of life care, and what matters in the end.

20. Legal issues in old age

21. What to expect from domiciliary care

22. When a care home is best

OTHER PILGRIMS' FRIEND SOCIETY BOOKS IN THIS SERIES: